The story of
VAISAKHI
The Birth of The Khalsa Panth

Author & Illustrator
Ishpal Kaur

Guru Gobind Singh Ji

Guru Gobind Singh Ji,
Is a Guru and a Disciple,
A Scholar and a true Warrior,
And humblest of us all.

Guru Gobind Singh Ji,
Who went to create something amazing,
Who sacrificed their entire family,
For the Khalsa Panth, they gave everything.

Guru Gobind Singh Ji,
Endless love and devotion for Vaheguru Ji,
Guru Gobind Singh Ji,
Our Guru Pita for eternity.

GURU GOBIND SINGH JI
THE TENTH GURU JI FOR SIKHS

Guru Gobind Singh Ji was born in 1666 in Patna Sahib, India. At the tender age of 9, they became the next Guru Ji for the Sikhs after their father Guru Tegh Bahadur Ji (ninth Guru Ji of the Sikh faith) was martyred for refusing to change their faith in Sikhi and for the freedom of choice of religion. Guru Gobind Singh Ji was very well versed in archery, martial arts, horsemanship, languages and much more. He had very good knowledge of other faiths and was extremely articulate. Guru Gobind Singh Ji respected other religions, but loved and honoured the Sikh faith, and in 1699 Guru Ji was about to create something spectacular. An army of compassionate, righteous, courageous, unwavering and truthful characters....

Guru Gobind Singh Ji (who were Guru Gobind Rai Ji at the time), wrote to the sangat (congregation) near and far special edict (order) letters months prior to the 1699 Vaisakhi harvest festival, ordering the sangat to come with uncut hair and with their heads covered to this year's Vaisakhi, as something very special was going to happen....
In 1699, on the 30th March (Chet - Panjabi calendar month) at Anandpur Sahib, the birth and uprise of the Khalsa Panth was about to take place....

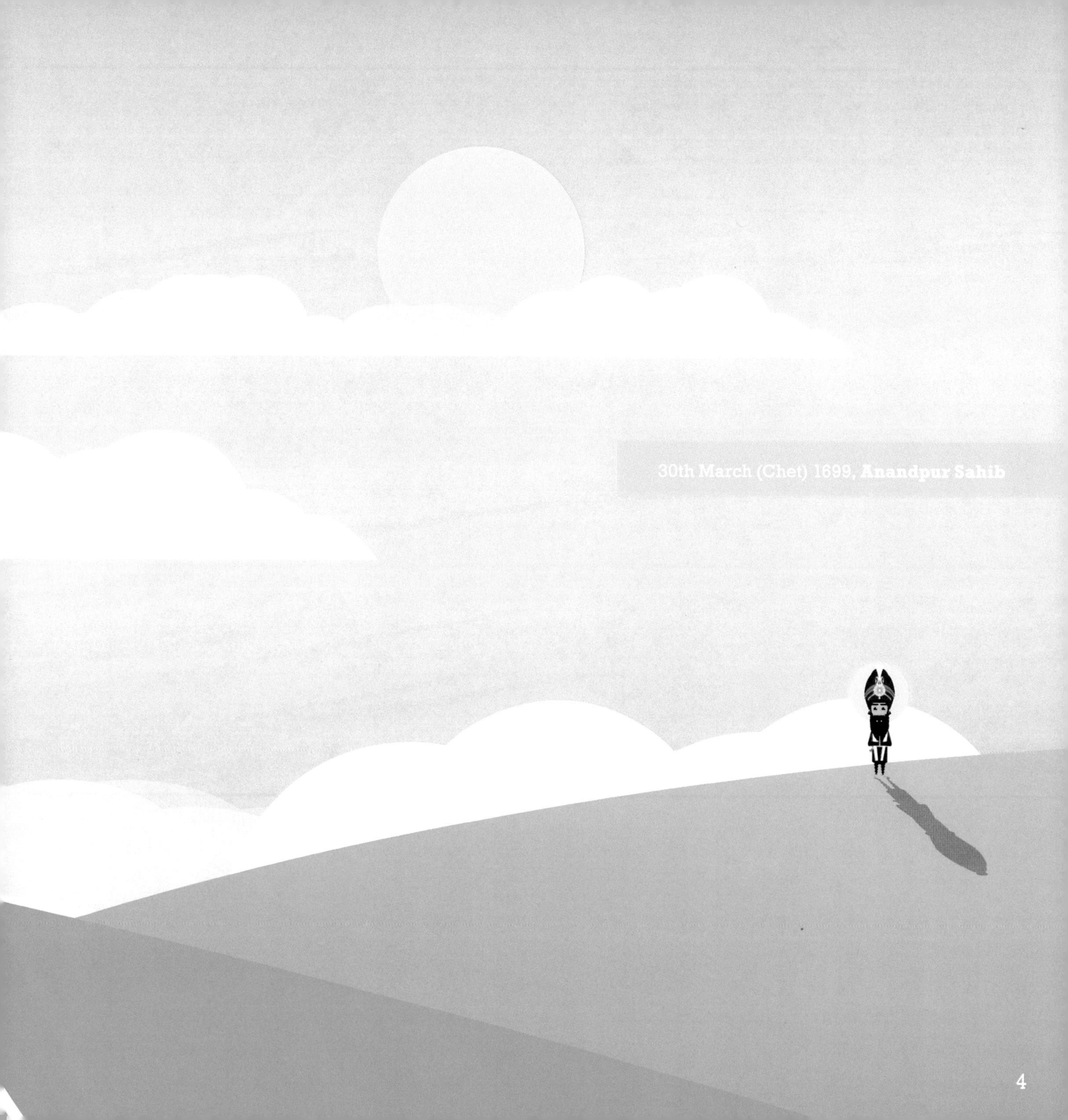
30th March (Chet) 1699, **Anandpur Sahib**

WHO, WILL GIVE THEIR HEAD?

WHO, WILL GIVE THEIR HEAD?

One **beloved** person rose…and with their hands clasped together, they apologised to Guru Ji for not coming forward on Guru Ji's first call.

Guru Gobind Singh Ji stood in front of thousands at Anandpur Sahib, after inviting them to come, proclaiming that this year's Vaisakhi will be different. Guru Ji, with a talvar (long sword) in their hand, asked the sangat, **"*Who* will give their head?"** Amongst the crowd, erupted shock and confusion.... Guru Ji repeated the same question, but no one rose. Guru Ji repeated the question once again, and then...

one person rose.

Guru Ji took Bhai Daya Ram, the first one to rise after Guru Ji's request for a head, into a tent, holding the talvar (long sword). A noise came from the tent.... The sangat (congregation) who were already shocked and confused from Guru Ji wanting a head, watched as Guru Ji walked from the tent with the talvar, covered in blood.... The sangat (congregation) were in dismay, but Guru Ji did not stop there, as they again asked, *"Who* **will give their head?"**....

SLASH

AFTER...

Guru Ji asked the question to the sangat (congregation) again, **"Who will give their head?"** Another brave man stood, and offered his head to Guru Ji. The sangat (congregation) were getting more and more shocked and confused now. *"What could Guru Ji be thinking"....* *"This is not right"....* *"Guru Ji knows what they are doing"....* Mixed thoughts were going through the sangat's (congregation) minds. Again, Guru Ji took them to the tent, whilst still holding the bloody talvar (long sword). After a noise that had come from the tent, Guru Ji came out alone, still holding the bloody talvar. Those that stood and offered their heads, did not know why Guru Ji was asking such a question, but they were still ready to give their lives, even after witnessing the outcome of Bhai Daya Ram, the first piyara (beloved) that stood tall. Guru Ji continued requesting for heads. How many heads did Guru Ji need?....

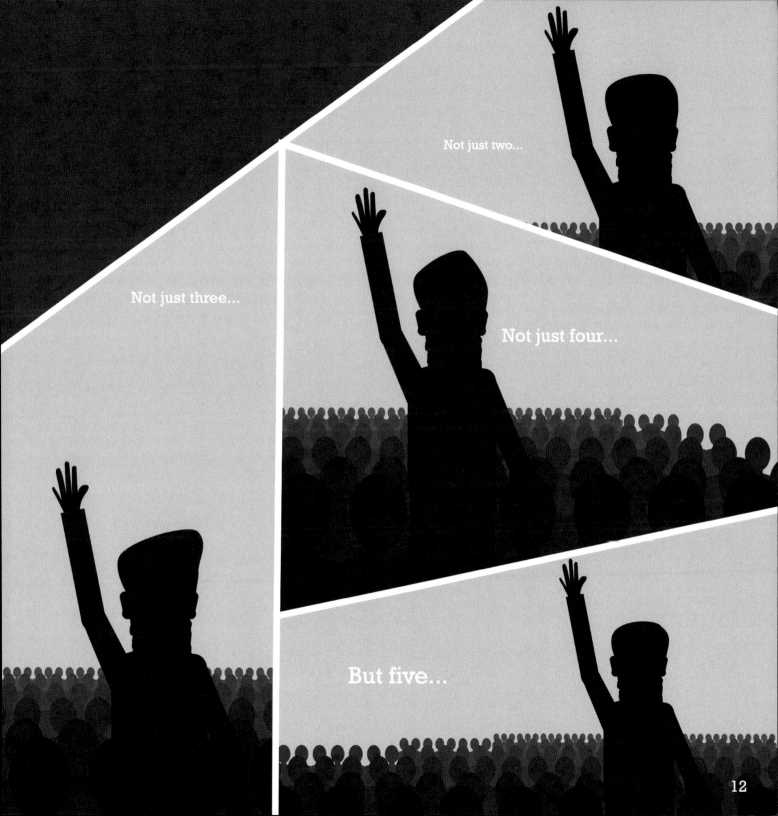

SLASH

SLASH

SLASH

SLASH

Mata Jeeto Ji

Japji Sahib, Jaap Sahib, Tav Prasad Savaiye, Chaupai Sahib and Anand Sahib.

KHANDI DI PAAHUL AMRIT
(Blessed nectar)

After five heads were offered to Guru Ji, something special was about to happen. Guru Ji asked for five heads, but those same five beloved were to be brought back to life by Guru Pita Ji. Using a double edged sarb-loh (metal) khanda (sword), as well as a sarb-loh (metal) paahul (bowl), Guru Pita Ji started preparing the Khandi Di Paahul Amrit (blessed nectar). *Water* was placed in the bowl and the Panj Baania paath (Gurbani - Guru Ji's teachings, from **Sri Guru Granth Sahib Ji** and **Sri Dasam Granth Sahib Ji** - composed by Guru Gobind Singh Ji): *Japji Sahib, Jaap Sahib, Tav Prasad Savaiye, Chaupai Sahib and Anand Sahib,* were recited whilst Guru Ji stirred the mixture. *Five pataseh* (sugar crystals) were bought by Mata Jeeto Ji, Guru Gobind Singh Ji's Dharam Patnee (wife), to be placed in the paahul (bowl), to add sweetness to this very strong, powerful amrit that was being prepared. Guru Ji wanted us to stay strong but also to remember to be sweet and humble within our character. Khandi Di Paahul Amrit (blessed nectar) was being prepared for the Amrit Sanchaar (baptism) ceremony. A ceremony that Guru Ji had been planning; where sparrows would rise to be lions....

The five that had offered their heads for **Guru Ji,** one by one, were
initiated by the hands of **Guru Gobind Singh Ji** with the *Khandi Di Paahul
Amrit* (blessed nectar), to create and become part of the *Khalsa Panth*
(pure path), to become the *'Panj Piyare (five beloved).'*

THE PANJ PIYARE
THE FIVE BELOVED

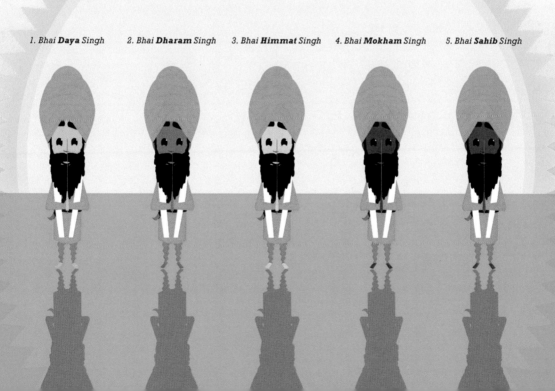

1. Bhai **Daya** Singh   2. Bhai **Dharam** Singh   3. Bhai **Himmat** Singh   4. Bhai **Mokham** Singh   5. Bhai **Sahib** Singh

INITIATION
AMRIT SANCHAAR (BAPTISM)
CEREMONY

The Amrit Sanchaar (baptism) ceremony was created by Guru Gobind Singh Ji because Guru Ji wanted to establish the Khalsa Panth (pure path, God's army). Those that were initiated were known as Amritdhari (baptised) Sikhs. The five beloved were initiated with Amrit and were blessed to be the *Panj Piyare*, the start of the *Khalsa Panth*.

Guru Ji wanted to annihilate injustice and oppression against mankind. From the time of Guru Nanak Dev Ji, up and until Guru Gobind Singh Ji, the flow of oppression and exploitation of religion conversion was still occurring. Guru Arjan Dev Ji (fifth Guru Ji) and Guru Tegh Bahadur Ji (ninth Guru Ji), gave Shaheedi (martyrdom) for such reasons, as they refused to change their faith. Guru Hargobind Ji (sixth Guru Ji) had initiated the Miri Piri concept (saint soldier), but now Guru Gobind Singh Ji was making a seal. They were making an identity for all Sikhs to become Khalsa **Singhs** (kings of the jungle; courageous and brave warriors), and Khalsa **Kaurs** (gracious and dignified warriors). Guru Gobind Singh Ji bestowed these names for the children of the Khalsa Panth, Guru Ji and Mata Sahib Devan Ji (Mata Sahib Kaur Ji) being the spiritual parents.

All walks of life were welcome to join the Panth, regardless of caste, status, gender, religion and location. The five beloved were pure examples of this. The Panj Piyare (five beloved) became Singhs, eradicating the stigma of any social attachments to surnames. We are all equal in the eyes of our Guru Ji, actions and sharda (faith) count, not caste or social tags that one may have in society. If there is any caste, then it is Khalsa, our identity and commitment to Guru Ji.

GURU GOBIND RAI JI
GURU GOBIND SINGH JI

Guru Gobind Singh Ji, gave the responsibility to the Panj Piyare to initiate others into the Khalsa Panth, including Guru Ji themself. Many were shocked at this, as they were the 'Guru', however, Guru Ji respected and showed that they too, would need to take Amrit to be part of the Khalsa Panth. With this example, Guru Ji proved, that they were not just the 'Guru', but also a 'Chela' (disciple) too. Guru Ji humbly received Amrit from the Panj Piyare, and then Guru Gobind Rai Ji became...**Guru Gobind Singh Ji.**

THE PANJ KAKAARS
The five K's

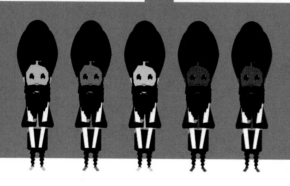

The Panj Kakaar were gifted to the Panj Piyare, and worn during the Amrit Sanchaar (baptism) ceremony. Each Kakaar is equally important, and they each have a purpose. All Kakaars are to be respected, kept clean, and are to be worn throughout an Amritdhari (baptised) Sikh's life.

Kanga
Comb (wooden)

A Kanga is a comb, and is used to help untangle the Kes (hair). It's also used to help keep the Kes (hair) clean, as well as tidy.

The Kanga (comb) is to be kept tucked firmly in the Kes (hair).

The purpose of the Kanga (comb) can be applied to our thoughts and actions: untangled, clean and tidy.

Kes
Hair (Head to toe)

Kes (hair) is a pivotal identity to the Sikh faith. It is to be kept in its most natural form, as well as uncut, and always kept clean.

The Kes is usually kept tied in a neat knot on top of the head.

The Kes is usually covered either with a Dastaar (turban), or a chunni (scarf). The Dastaar is also part of the Sikh faith's identity.

Kara
Bangle (Metal)

The Kara is a sarb-loh (metal) bangle, and it is to be worn on the wrist(s).

The Kara is to help remind us not to do wrong. Like an axis, the Kara is to help keep us grounded.

The wearing of a Kara is a constant reminder of how our hands, should be to serve Guru Ji.

Kirpaan
Sword (Metal)

The Kirpaan is a sarb-loh (metal) sword. It can be worn with the use of kamar-kasa (waistband), or a gatra (strap) that goes across the body.

The Kirpaan is a sign of a saint-soldier.

We should help protect ourselves and other's dignity. Having self respect is important.

Kachera
Undergarment

The Kachera is an undergarment. It is worn to help cover the individual modestly. The length of it, can extend up to the knee.

The Kachera is a modest undergarment, and this modesty can be applied to how we live our lives.

It can also help set boundaries of self control, helping us towards our life commitment to Guru Ji.

About of...

BHAI DAYA SINGH

The **first** Panj Piyare

- Kindness
- Compassion
- Humility

- Caring
- Understanding
- Empathy

{ Compassion

BEFORE AMRIT SANCHAAR (BAPTISM) -

Name: *Bhai Daya Ram*
Age: *38*
D.O.B: *1661*
Caste: *Khatri* (shop keeper)
Town: *Lahore*

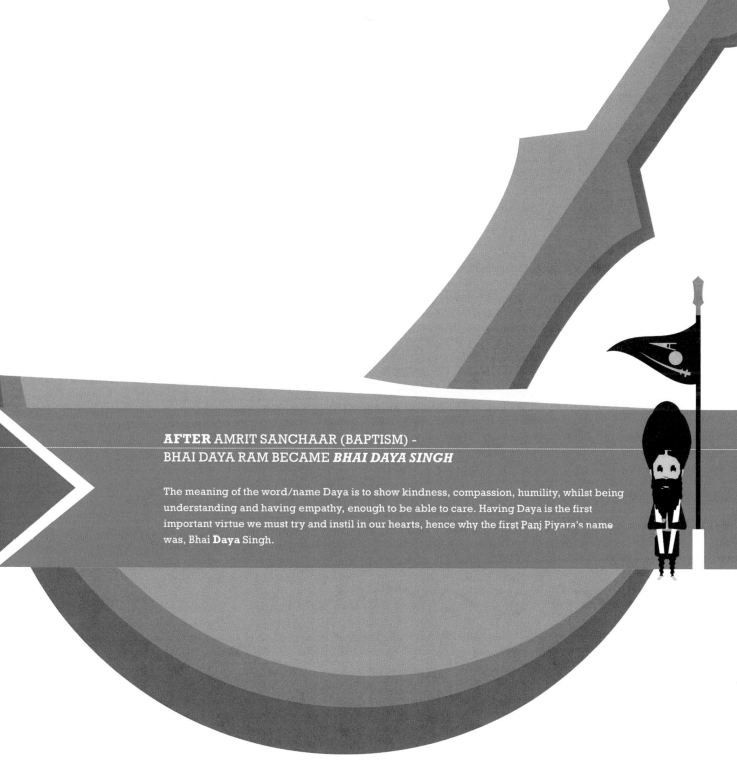

AFTER AMRIT SANCHAAR (BAPTISM) -
BHAI DAYA RAM BECAME *BHAI DAYA SINGH*

The meaning of the word/name Daya is to show kindness, compassion, humility, whilst being understanding and having empathy, enough to be able to care. Having Daya is the first important virtue we must try and instil in our hearts, hence why the first Panj Piyara's name was, Bhai **Daya** Singh.

BHAI DHARAM SINGH

The **second** Panj Piyare

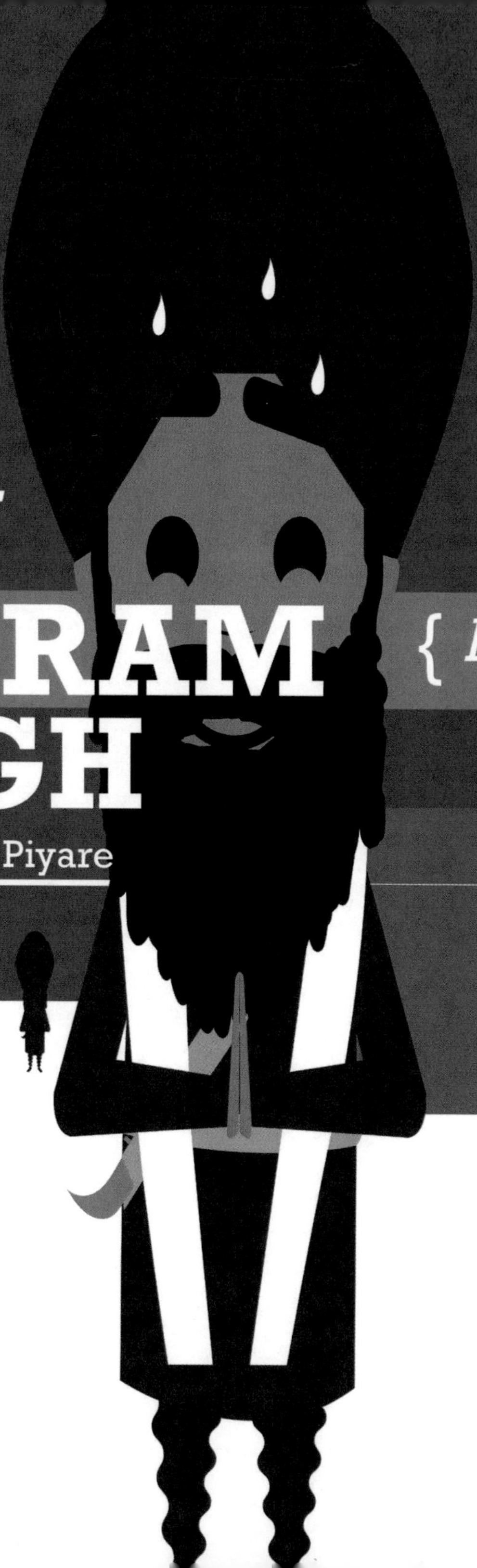

{ *Righteousness*

- Service
- Ethical
- Principled
- Moral
- Responsible
- Justice

BEFORE AMRIT SANCHAAR (BAPTISM) -

Name: *Bhai Dharam Das*
Age: *33*
D.O.B: *1666*
Caste: *Brahmin* (priest)
Town: *Hastinapur*

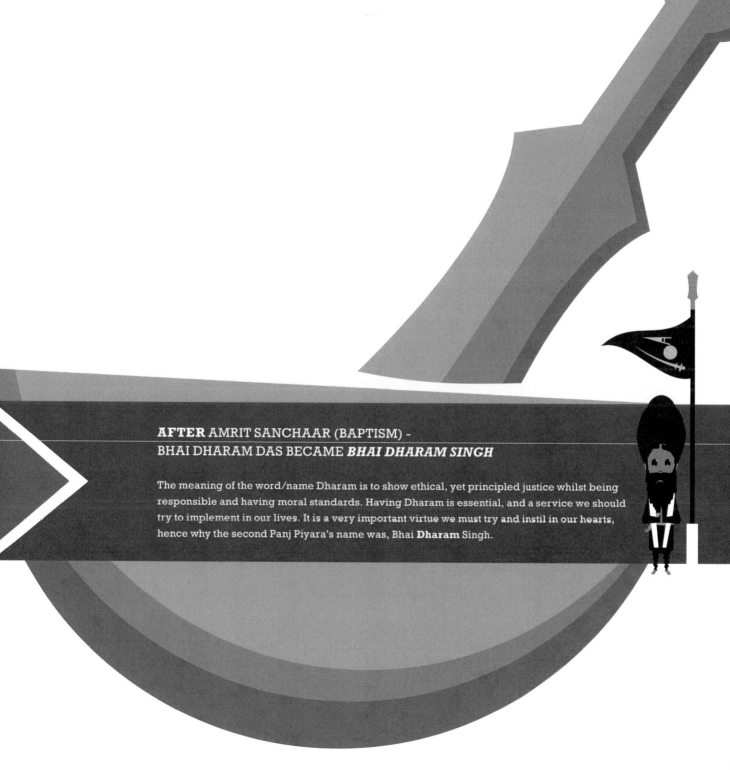

AFTER AMRIT SANCHAAR (BAPTISM) -
BHAI DHARAM DAS BECAME *BHAI DHARAM SINGH*

The meaning of the word/name Dharam is to show ethical, yet principled justice whilst being responsible and having moral standards. Having Dharam is essential, and a service we should try to implement in our lives. It is a very important virtue we must try and instil in our hearts, hence why the second Panj Piyara's name was, Bhai **Dharam** Singh.

BHAI HIMMAT SINGH

The **third** Panj Piyare

- Fearless
- Brave
- Warrior
- Valiant
- Courageous
- Strength

{ *Courageous*

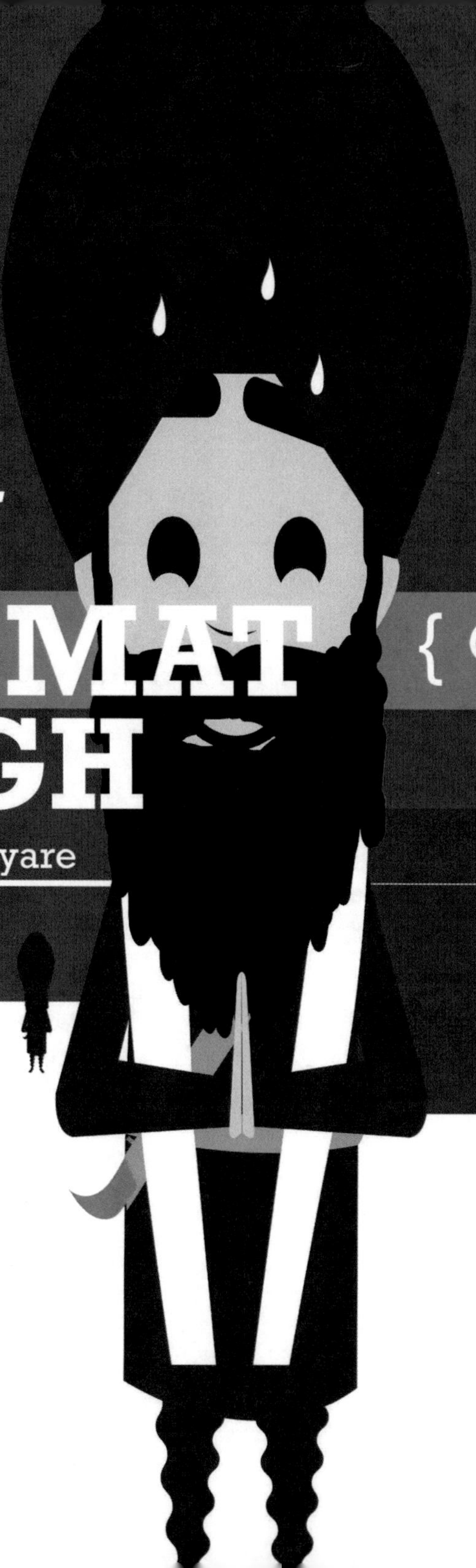

BEFORE AMRIT SANCHAAR (BAPTISM) -

Name: *Bhai Himmat Rai*
Age: *38*
D.O.B: *1661*
Caste: *Ghumar* (water carrier)
Town: *Orissa*

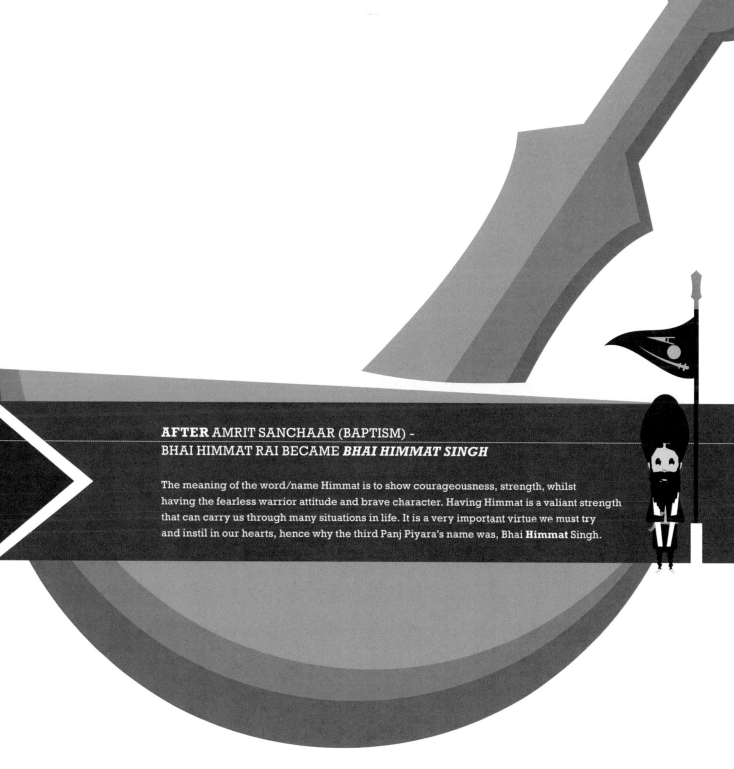

AFTER AMRIT SANCHAAR (BAPTISM) -
BHAI HIMMAT RAI BECAME *BHAI HIMMAT SINGH*

The meaning of the word/name Himmat is to show courageousness, strength, whilst having the fearless warrior attitude and brave character. Having Himmat is a valiant strength that can carry us through many situations in life. It is a very important virtue we must try and instil in our hearts, hence why the third Panj Piyara's name was, Bhai **Himmat** Singh.

About of...

BHAI MOKHAM SINGH

The **fourth** Panj Piyare

- Dedication
- Unchangeable
- Steadfast
- Abiding
- Determination
- Unwavering

{ *Determination*

BEFORE AMRIT SANCHAAR (BAPTISM) -

Name: *Bhai Mokham Rai*
Age: *36*
D.O.B: *1663*
Caste: **Chhimbar** (calico-printer)
Town: **Gujrat**

29

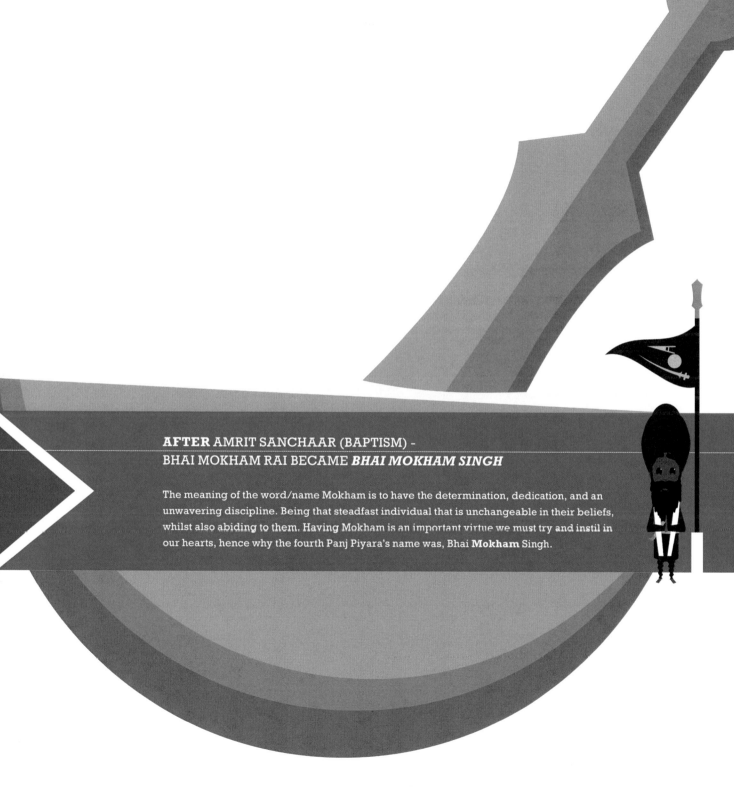

AFTER AMRIT SANCHAAR (BAPTISM) -
BHAI MOKHAM RAI BECAME *BHAI MOKHAM SINGH*

The meaning of the word/name Mokham is to have the determination, dedication, and an
unwavering discipline. Being that steadfast individual that is unchangeable in their beliefs,
whilst also abiding to them. Having Mokham is an important virtue we must try and instil in
our hearts, hence why the fourth Panj Piyara's name was, Bhai **Mokham** Singh.

BHAI SAHIB SINGH

The **fifth** Panj Piyare

- Joyous
- Happiness
- Conqueror
- Forever
- Eternal Bliss
- Timeless

{ **Eternal Bliss**

BEFORE AMRIT SANCHAAR (BAPTISM) -

Name: *Bhai Sahib Chand*
Age: *37*
D.O.B: *1662*
Caste: *Nai* (barber)
Town: *Karnataka*

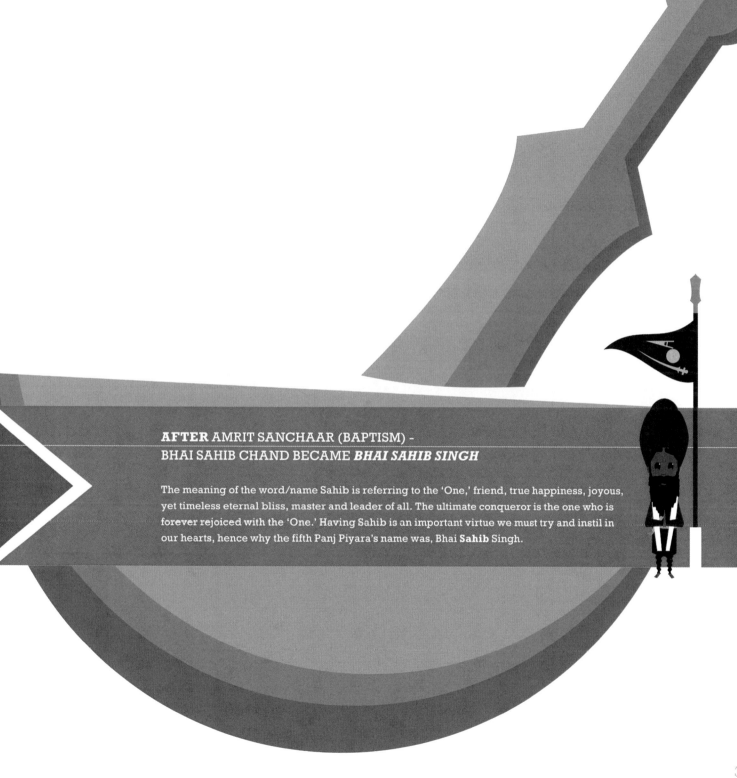

AFTER AMRIT SANCHAAR (BAPTISM) -
BHAI SAHIB CHAND BECAME *BHAI SAHIB SINGH*

The meaning of the word/name Sahib is referring to the 'One,' friend, true happiness, joyous, yet timeless eternal bliss, master and leader of all. The ultimate conqueror is the one who is forever rejoiced with the 'One.' Having Sahib is an important virtue we must try and instil in our hearts, hence why the fifth Panj Piyara's name was, Bhai **Sahib** Singh.

Vaheguru Ji Ka **Khalsa**
Vaheguru Ji Ki **Fateh!**

The Khalsa belongs to Vaheguru Ji and so does the victory. The Khalsa was formed by Guru Gobind Singh Ji after being ordained by Akaal Purakh (God). The Khalsa Panth went on to fight many battles against unrighteous, oppressive and exploitative acts towards mankind. The Khalsa Panth attacks only as the last resort. Being humble, yet assertive and courageous is honourable, and having self respect for ourselves and others is important.

The Panj Piyare

The Panj Piyare,
Who gave their lives for Guru Ji,
Who had so much love and devotion,
That they gave their heads; lives for Thee.

The Khalsa Panth,
Was gifted, for the sacrifices they made,
And went to fight many battles,
After the Khalsa Panth was made.

Oppression was still apparent,
And the Panth was now, forever,
Being the true saint soldiers,
Fighting for righteousness, to endeavour.

DEGH TEGH **FATEH**
Victory of **food** and **protection**

PANTH KI **JEET**
Victory of the **Khalsa Panth**

RAJ KEREGA **KHALSA**
Victory of **righteousness**
(A place of food, justice,
freedom and protection.)

The **Khalsa Panth**

Guru Gobind Singh Ji,
Asked for five heads,
Each beloved stood tall,
And graciously offered their heads....

They gave their lives,
They gave everything for their Guru Ji,
But Guru Ji had something planned,
And then gave them new lives to be....

Guru Gobind Singh Ji,
After the Hukam from Akaal,
Created the Khalsa Panth,
The army of Akaal....

The Khalsa Panth, The five beloved,
The Panth of justice and truth,
The Panth that Guru Ji was ordained to create,
For everyone, the elder and the youth....

They were the Guru Ji,
They were the Tenth Master,
But they were also a Disciple too,
And bowed in front of the Khalsa....

What will Guru Ji sacrifice,
As the Panj Piyare each gave their head,
Guru Ji gave up their entire family,
For the Khalsa Panth to move ahead....

Sacrifices were made,
To uphold the righteous need,
For the Khalsa Guru Ji gave everything,
So they could plant the righteous seed....

Khalsa is Guru Ji's Pachaan,
Khalsa is Guru Ji's life to be,
Khalsa is Guru Ji's everything,
Khalsa is Guru Ji's identity....

Khalsa is for everyone,
Khalsa is about truth,
Khalsa is about justice,
Khalsa is forever youth....

OUR
GURU JI
TENTH **MASTER**

1) Do you know the
name of the tenth Master?

2) *Where* was the tenth
Master born?

3) Do you know *when* the
tenth Master was born?

KHALSA
PANTH
PURE **PATH**

1) Who *created* the
Khalsa Panth?

2) Do you know *when* the
Khalsa Panth was
formed?

3) Do you know *why* the
Khalsa Panth was
formed?

KHANDI DI
PAHUL **AMRIT**
BLESSED **NECTAR**

1) Do you know the
ingredients of the Khandi
Di Pahul Amrit?

2) Do you know the
names of each Bani that
was recited whilst making
the Amrit?

3) Do you know *why* the
pataseh were added to
the Amrit?

AMRIT
SANCHAAR
BAPTISM **CEREMONY**

1) Do you know *why* the
Amrit Sanchaar was
happening?

2) Do you know *why* Guru
Ji also asked to be
blessed with Amrit?

3) Do you know who then
baptised Guru Ji?

THE PANJ
SEES
THE **FIVE HEADS**

1) Do you know *who* the
first beloved was to give
their head?

2) How did the sangat
react to Guru Ji's requests?

2) How did Guru Ji
take each head?

THE PANJ
PIYARE
THE **FIVE BELOVED**

1) Do you know the
names of each Panj
Piyara?

2) Do you know the
meanings of each Panj
Piyara's name?

3) *What* additional name
did Guru Ji give to the
Panj Piyare?

BOLE...SO NIHAAL! SAT *SRI* AKAAL!

SPEAK OF... *JOYOUS SUCCESS!* OF THE **TRUE ONE!**

Vaheguru Ji Ka **Khalsa!**
Vaheguru Ji Ki **Fateh!**

Author & Illustrator
Ishpal Kaur

Disclaimer: 'The story of Vaisakhi' - The Birth of The Khalsa Panth, story information book, was created with the intent to help educate Sikhs and non-Sikhs about the Sikh faith. Ishpal Kaur Dhillon does not hold any responsibility or liability for any indirect or direct damage or harm caused, due to the contents of this book. Ishpal Kaur Dhillon apologises for any unintentional mistakes, as well as any unintentional misunderstandings, in regards to the contents of this book.

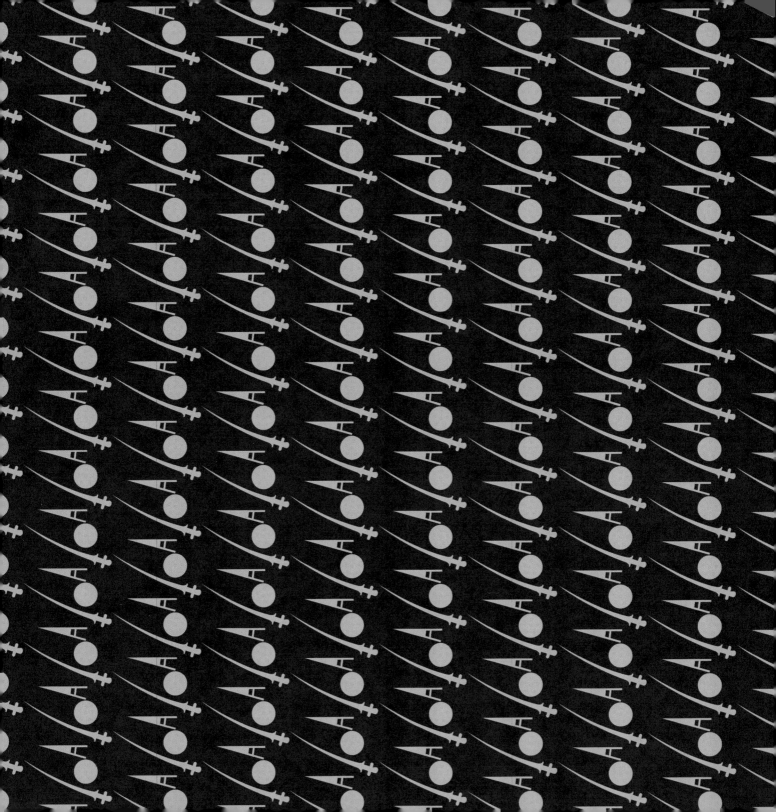

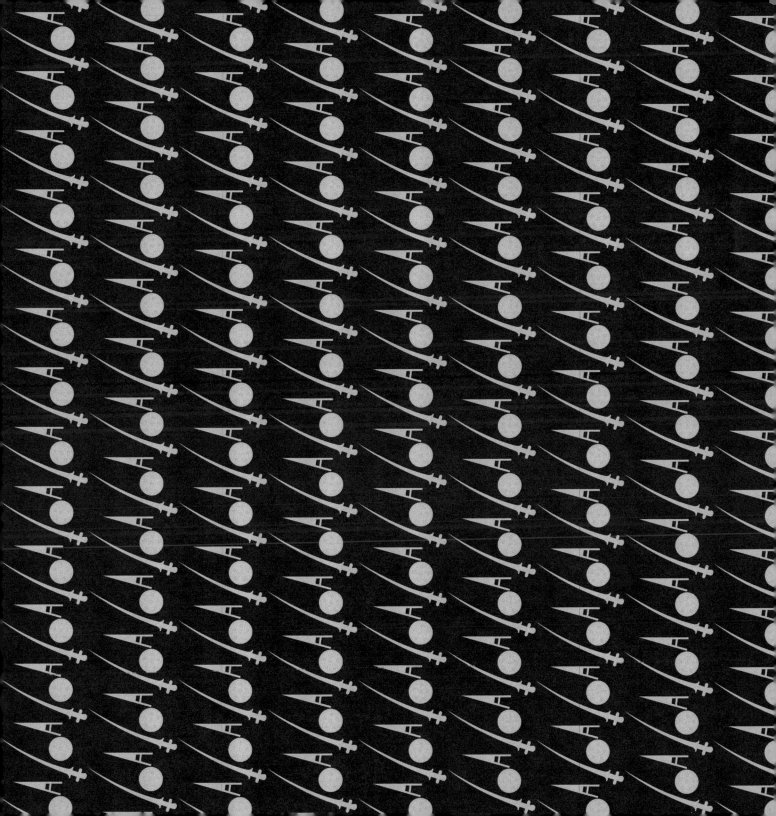

Made in the USA
Las Vegas, NV
25 April 2022